This book belongs to

. . . .

Copyright © 2021

make believe ideas ltd

The Wilderness, Berkhamsted, Hertfordshire, HP4 2AZ, UK.

www.makebelieveideas.co.uk

Photographs courtesy of Shutterstock.

The animal band

by Alexandra Robinson

make
believe
ideas

Get the most from this reader

Before reading:

- Look at the pictures and discuss them together. Ask questions such as, "What instrument is this hedgehog playing?"

- Relate the topic to your child's world. For example, say: "What songs do we listen to?"

- Familiarise your child with book vocabulary by using terms such as *word*, *letter*, *title*, *author* and *text*.

During reading:

- Prompt your child to sound out unknown words. Draw attention to neglected middle or end sounds.

- Encourage your child to use the pictures as clues to unknown words.

- Occasionally ask what might happen next, and then check together as you read on.

- Monitor your child's understanding. Repeated readings can improve fluency and comprehension.

- Keep reading sessions short and enjoyable. Stop if your child becomes tired or frustrated.

• •

After reading:

- Discuss the book. Encourage your child to form opinions with questions such as, "What did you like best about this book?"

- Help your child work through the fun activities at the back of the book. Then ask him or her to reread the story. Praise any improvement.

The animals like music.
The **cat** is playing
the guitar.
She is in the band.

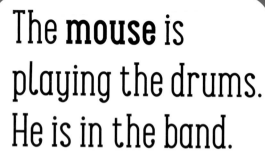

The **mouse** is playing the drums. He is in the band.

The **monkey** is singing.
He is in the band.

The **fox** is dancing.
He is in the band.

The **squirrel** is playing the horn. She is in the band.

The animals put on a show. They are all in the **band**.

Discussion Questions

1. What colour is the band's uniform?

2. Which animal plays the drums?

3. Would you like to be in a band? Why?

꒰ Sight Words ꒱

Learning sight words helps you read fluently. Practise these sight words from the book. Use them in sentences of your own.

on

they

all

a

in

is

the

are

Rhyming Words

Can you find the rhyming pairs?
Say them aloud.

be

hat

hand

he

cat

band

25

Writing Practice

Read the words, and then trace
them with your finger.

like

show

band

26

music

drums

piano

❧ Silly Sentences ❧

Have fun filling in the gap in each sentence. Use the ideas below or make up your own.

The hedgehog is playing the ....

The fox is ....